10 Kang

by Jane Manners
illustrated by Laura Ovresat

Harcourt

Orlando   Boston   Dallas   Chicago   San Diego

www.harcourtschool.com

10 kangaroos take a ride at eleven.

2

3 jump out. Now there are

7. Seven kangaroos go for a drive.

2 jump out and now there are

5. Five kangaroos ride to a store.

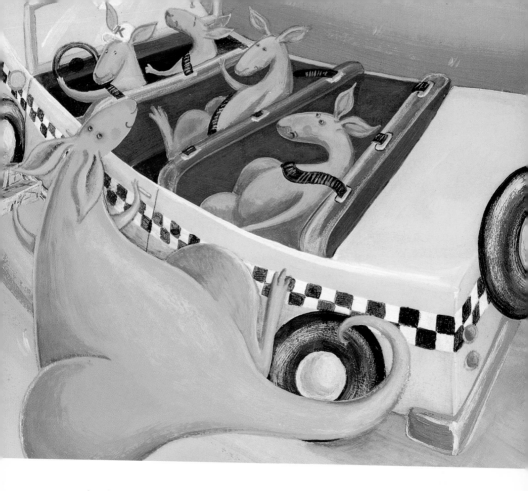

1 jumps out and now there are

4.

Four kangaroos are out for some fun.

3 jump out and now there is

1. One kangaroo stops on a hill.

He jumps out, but wait

there's Bill!